782.42 Aw
MAD

KU-747-775

Mad World
+ 9 Smash Hits

SBN 0-7119-2704-9

This book © Copyright 2004 by Wise Publications,
/9 Frith Street, London W1D 3JB.

Unauthorised reproduction of any part of this publication by
any means including photocopying is an infringement of copyright.

Compiled by Nick Crispin.
Cover photographs courtesy of
D Communications & London Features International.
Printed in the United Kingdom.

Millennium Centre

00230139

**This publication is not authorised for sale in the
United States of America and / or Canada**

Mad World

Words & Music by Roland Orzabal

Cello 2° only till *

© Copyright 1982 Roland Orzabal Limited/Chrysalis Music Limited.
All Rights Reserved. International Copyright Secured.

go - ing no - where, go - ing no - where.____ Their tears are fill - ing
sit and lis - ten, sit and lis - ten.____ Went to school and I was

up their glass - es, no ex - pres - sion, no ex - pres - sion.____
ve - ry ner - vous, no - one knew__ me, no - one knew__ me.____

Hide my head, I wan - na drown my sor - row, no to - mor - row,
Hel - lo teach - er, tell me what's my les - son, look right through__ me,

no to - mor - row.____ And I find it kin - da fun - ny, I find it kin - da
look right through me.____

Jump (For My Love)

Words & Music by Gary Skardina, Marti Sharron & Stephen Mitchell

1. Your eyes___ tell___ me how you

© Copyright 1983 Anidraks Music/Stephen Mitchell Music/Welbeck Music Corporation, USA.
Sony/ATV Music Publishing (UK) Limited (33.34%)/Warner/Chappell Music Limited (33.33%)/EMI Music Publishing Limited (33.33%).
All Rights Reserved. International Copyright Secured.

want me; I can feel__ it in your heart - beat.

I know__ you like__ what you see.

2. Hold me,__ I'll give__ you all that you need.
(3.) told me__ I'm the on - ly wo - man for you;

Wrap__ your love a - round me. You're so ex - cit - ed I can
no - bo - dy does it like I do. Then make a move be - fore you

feel you get - ting hot - ter.   Oh, ba - by.   I'll___ take   you down,
try and go much fur - ther.   Oh, ba - by.   You__ are the one,

I'll   take   you down_____   where no - one's ev - er gone_ be - fore.__
you   are   the one,_____   and Hea - ven waits here at__ my   door.

And if you want   more,___   if you want   more,___   more,_   more,_

yeah!   Jump   for__ my love.__   Jump in__

jump_____ for_____ my love._____

3. You

When you_ are

next_____ to me,_____ oh I come a - live._____

Your love burns in -

- side.

Oh, it feels so____ right.____

Come to me if you want me to - night._____

_____ Jump.

I know my heart can make you hap - py.____ (Jump in.)

You know these arms, they fill you up. (Jump.)

If you wan - na taste my kiss - es in the night, then____

____ jump____ for____ my love.____

Changes

Words & Music by Ozzy Osbourne, Tony Iommi, Terry Butler & Bill Ward

(Kelly) I'm feel-in' hap-py,___ I am so sad,___

I lost the best friend that I ev-er had.___

© Copyright 1972 Onward Music Limited.
All Rights Reserved. International Copyright Secured.

Leave Right Now

Words & Music by Francis White

© Copyright 2003 Universal Music Publishing Limited.
All Rights Reserved. International Copyright Secured.

I would-n't know_ how to say how_____ good it feels see-ing you to-day,

and see you've got your smile_ back,_ like_ you say you're right on track, but

you may ne - ver know_ why once_ bit-ten twice is shy,_

if I'm proud per-haps I should ex-plain I could-n't bear to lose you a-

I think I be-ter leave right____ now._____ Yes I will.

I think I be-ter leave____ right now,____ I'm feel-ing weak-er and weak-er,

some-bo-dy bet-ter show____ me____ how_____ be-fore I fall a-ny deep-er,

rall.

I think I bet-ter leave right____ now.

Not Me, Not I

Words & Music by Delta Goodrem, Eliot Kennedy, Gary Barlow & Kara Dioguardi

© Copyright 2003 Sony/ATV Music Publishing (UK) Limited (60%)/EMI Music Publishing Limited (35%)/Copyright Control (5%).
All Rights Reserved. International Copyright Secured.

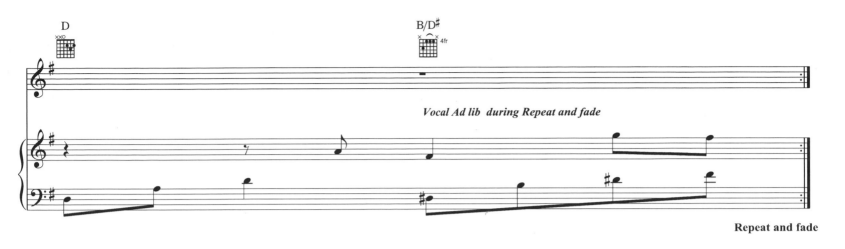

Vocal Ad lib during Repeat and fade

Repeat and fade

(Additional lyrics)

Verse 2

The story goes on without you.
There's got to be another ending.
Yeah, you broke my heart, it won't be the last time.
But I"ll get over them too.
As a new door opens we close the ones behind,
And if you search your soul I know you'll find,
You never really knew me.

One More Chance

Words & Music by R. Kelly

© Copyright 2003 R. Kelly Publishing Incorporated, USA.
Zomba Music Publishers Limited.
All Rights Reserved. International Copyright Secured.

Repeat and fade

Verse 2
Searching, for that one who is going to make me whole,
Help me make these mysteries unfold.
Hold on.
Lightning, about to strike in rain only on me.
Hurts so bad, sometimes it's hard to breathe.
Oh why, why?

If you see her *etc*.

Life For Rent

Words & Music by Dido & Rollo Armstrong

1. I have-n't ev-er real-ly found a place that I call home,   I
(2.) al-ways thought that I would love to live by the sea,   to

nev-er stick a-round quite long e-nough to make it.   I a-
tra-vel the world a-lone and live more simp-ly.   I have

-po-lo-gise where once a-gain I'm not in love,   but it's not as if I
no i-dea what's hap-pened to that dream   but as there's

© Copyright 2003 Warner/Chappell Music Limited (80%)/BMG Music Publishing Limited (20%).
All Rights Reserved. International Copyright Secured.

mind that your_ heart ain't ex - act - ly break __ ing.
real - ly no - thing left here_____ to stop me,

It's just a thought,_
it's just a thought,_

__ on - ly a thought_____
__ on - ly a thought_____

that if my

life_____ is___ for___ rent,

and I

don't learn to buy,_____

well, I de - serve___

38

D.S. al Coda

Well how can I____ say I'm a-live.____ Well if my

Coda

'cause no-thing I_____ have_____ is tru - ly mine,____

'cause no-thing I_____ have_____ is tru - ly mine,____

N.C.

'cause no-thing I_____ have_____ is tru - ly mine.____

Santa Cruz (You're Not That Far)

Words by Conor Deasy
Music by Conor Deasy, Kevin Horan, Pádraic McMahon, Daniel Ryan & Ben Carrigan

© Copyright 2003 BMG Music Publishing Limited.
All Rights Reserved. International Copyright Secured.

San - ta Cruz,___ no, you're not that far.___ 2. But

Banjo

The Voice Within

Words & Music by Christina Aguilera & Glen Ballard

© Copyright 2002 Xtina Music/Aerostation Corporation/MCA Music Publishing Incorporated, USA.
BMG Music Publishing Limited (50%)/Universal/MCA Music Limited (50%).
All Rights Reserved. International Copyright Secured.

find the strength___ that will guide_____ your way___ if you'll learn___ to be-gin_____ to

trust the voice with - in._____

Young girl, don't cry;___ I'll be___ right here___ when your___ world starts to fall.___

Ooh,_____

mm.

Slow

Words & Music by Emiliana Torrini, Kylie Minogue & Daniel Carey

Knew you'd be here to - night, so I put___ my best dress on. Boy, I was so___

___ right.___ Our eyes con - nect - ed; now no - thing's how___

© Copyright 2003 Warner/Chappell Music Limited (66.67%)/The International Music Network Limited (33.33%).
All Rights Reserved. International Copyright Secured.

it used to be,__ no se - cond guess - es.__   Track in on this feel-

- ing,____   full fo - cus close____ up you__ and me; no - bo - dy's leav-
__ it,____   let the rhy - thm pull__ you in.__ It's here, so touch__

- ing.____   Got me af - fect - ed,____   spun me one__
__ it.____   Y'know what I'm say - ing,____   and I have-

__ eight - y__ de - grees;__ it's so el - ec - tric.__ }
- n't said a thing.__ Keep the re - cord play - ing.__ }
     Slow down and

dance with me___   yeah,_____   slow.___

___   Skip a beat and

move with my bo - dy;___   yeah,_____   slow.___

Come on and dance with me,___   yeah,_____   slow.__